Teaching

KIDS

the Engineering Design Process

*with ten fun hands-on projects
for grades 3-5*

© 2024 Innate Press
www.innatepress.com

Table of Contents

Note to the Teacher

Welcome to the exciting world of engineering design! Your students will enjoy these hands-on building projects while learning the design process, vocabulary, and scientific principles. Kids will enjoy building structures, materials, and tools by trying different things and improving their designs with iteration. Social interaction and discussion helps solidify the engineering and science concepts learned along the way! These lessons are wonderful for encouraging the development of problem-solving skills and growth mindset.

Each project includes comprehensive lesson plans, collaborative small group activities, and class discussion. In addition to hands-on activities, each lesson includes a student instruction sheet, a student response sheet, extension activities, and resources that provide opportunities for further exploration.

Some extension activities and resources include videos or other elements that are accessed through the internet. These links are given when the link is clear (not a bunch of letters and numbers!). For complex links, we provided the title that should show up easily with an internet search. You can also access all the links mentioned on our website by scanning the code below or going to the website: www.innatepress.com/teaching-kids-the-engineering-design-process

We hope you enjoy seeing the innovative designs your students come up with!

Innate Press

Spaghetti Structures

Spaghetti Structures

Lesson

Spaghetti Structures: Exploring Stability and Engineering Design

Objectives

Students will:
- Identify the meaning of the Latin root "struct" and the associated vocabulary words: structure and construct.
- Compare and evaluate multiple structures according to the goals of height and stability.
- Apply the engineering design principles to test, discuss, evaluate, and redesign their structures.

Materials

- Uncooked spaghetti noodles (1 box per group of 3-4 kids)
- Mini marshmallows (1 bag per group)
- Rulers or measuring tape
- Printed student instructions and response sheets (per group)

Vocabulary

- Latin root: "struct"
  - Structure
  - Construct
- Stable
- Engineering design
- Configuration

Spaghetti Structures

Introduction

Begin by asking students if they know the Latin root "struct." If not, give them some words that include this root such as: structure, construct, destruction, or unstructured. Lead the discussion to help them discover that "struct" means "build."

You may have the class brainstorm more words that contain the root "struct."

Mention the vocabulary word **structure**. Explain that a structure is something that is built with a particular pattern or shape. Structural engineers design buildings, bridges, and other structures to be strong and stable. Explain that **stable** means firmly fixed and unlikely to move or change.

The Challenge

Let the students know that today they will **construct** their own structures using materials they may usually find in their kitchens at home.

They will use spaghetti noodles as beams and marshmallows as connectors. You may want to demonstrate how to insert a stick of spaghetti into the marshmallow. Connections will be more **stable** if the spaghetti is pushed most of the way into the marshmallow. Students are allowed to break the spaghetti as needed.

Groups will be trying to make their structures as tall as possible, while making sure they are stable enough not to fall over.

Encourage the students to experiment with different designs and configurations.

Spaghetti Structures

Group Work: Phase 1 (15 min)

- Divide students into small groups of 3-4 people.
- Distribute the spaghetti noodles, marshmallows, and rulers or measuring tape to each group.
- Distribute the student response pages and ask students to draw some of their initial designs in the top section.
- Instruct students to plan and construct their spaghetti structures, keeping stability in mind.
- Circulate among the groups to provide guidance, answer questions, and facilitate discussions about the designs.

Testing (10 min)

Encourage the groups to create at least three different designs and assess their heights and stability. What configuration is the most stable? What design gives the best height without falling?

Students note the height of their designs on their response sheets and record their thoughts.

Have the groups combine features of their different designs to create their final, best design configuration to share with the rest of the class.

Circulate among the groups to help facilitate their discussions and decision process.

Have students draw, measure, and note the details about their final structures on the student response sheet.

Class Discussion (15 min)

- Bring the class back together to share and discuss.
- Discuss the design process with the class. Engineers try different solutions to engineering problems and test those solutions in order to come up with improved designs.
- Have groups share their best designs and talk about what worked for them and what didn't work.
- Allow other groups to comment or ask questions.
- Ask guiding questions to help student reflect on their designs:
  - How did you decide on the design of your structure?
  - What factors did you consider?
  - What was the most challenging aspect of building your structure? Why?
  - Did you encounter any problems or unexpected issues during the construction process? How did you handle those problems?
  - What type of base was the most stable?
  - What changes did you make to improve your initial designs?
  - How did working in a group impact the design and evaluation process? What were the advantages and challenges of collaborating on this project?

Spaghetti Structures

Optional: Group Work: Phase 2

If you have enough time, you can allow small groups to use their new knowledge to design one more structure.

If you have limited time, you can ask the students what improvements or modifications they would make if they were to build the structure again based on what they learned from the other groups in the class.

Conclusion (5 minutes)

Recap the key concepts learned during the activity, emphasizing the importance of stability in construction.

Go over the engineering design process steps of discussion, design, testing, and redesign.

Encourage students to think about how engineering principles impact the design and stability of various structures.

Point out books in the classroom or school library that relate to engineering, construction, and other related topics.

Review the Latin root "struct" and the vocabulary words: "structure" and "stable."

Collect the student response sheets.

Student Instructions

Spaghetti Structures

Follow the directions to take on the challenge!

As a group, you will build several structures using uncooked spaghetti noodles and marshmallows!

1. Discuss what shape the base should be. Remember that you want your structure to be stable.

2. Talk about how to build your structure to make it tall without causing it to fall over.

3. Try three different structures and measure their heights.

4. Draw your designs and write down their heights on your response sheet.

5. Discuss what you have learned from your three initial designs.

6. Decide upon your final design using what you have learned.

7. Build your final design.

8. Draw and note the height measurement of your final design on the student response sheet.

9. Write about what configuration worked best and why.

10. Prepare to share your design with the class!

Student Response Sheet

Names: _____

Spaghetti Structures

Follow the directions to take on the challenge!

Design 1

Height: _____

Design 2

Height: _____

Design 3

Height: _____

Final Design

Height: _____

What configuration worked best? Why?

_____

_____

_____

_____

_____

_____

15

© Innate Press

Spaghetti Structures

Extension Activities

- Repeat the activity, but instead of building structures for height and stability, focus on being able to carry the greatest load (using coins or other weights).

- Challenge students to build structures with enough stability to withstand simulated earthquakes (shaking the table).

- Explore different shapes and their impact on stability by encouraging students to build structures with triangles, squares, or arches.

- Try building with other materials such as:
    - Toothpicks and gumdrops
    - Straws and tape
    - Popsicle sticks and play dough
    - Pipe cleaners

- Take a field trip to a construction site

- Invite a guest speaker that is an architect, structural engineer, civil engineer, or builder to discuss building stable structures.

- Browse the Guinness Book of World Records related to structures, including the world's largest playing card structure: guinnessworldrecords.com/records/showcase/structures

Spaghetti Structures

Resources

- For teacher inspiration, check out this TED Talk:
  www.ted.com/talks/tom_wujec_build_a_tower_build_a_team
- Students may enjoy playing this app:
  www.commonsensemedia.org/app-reviews/spaghetti-marshmallows
- Read or provide some of the following books for your class to explore:
    - Bridges! Amazing Structures by Carol Johmann and Elizabeth Rieth
    - Skyscrapers! Super Structures by Carol Johmann
    - How Was That Built?: The Stories Behind Awesome Structures by Roma Agrawal and Katie Hickey
    - DK Great Buildings
    - DK Architecture: A Visual History by Jonathan Glancey
    - DK Engineers: From the Great Pyramids to the Pioneers of Space Travel
    - Castle by David Macaulay
    - The Way Things Work by David Macaulay

Design a Water Filter

Design a Water Filter

Lesson

Design a Water Filter: Exploring Environmental Engineering

Objectives

Students will:
- Understand the importance of water filtration in providing clean and safe drinking water.
- Design and create a functional water filtration instrument using a water bottle and various materials.
- Test and evaluate the effectiveness of their instrument.
- Collaborate, think critically, and apply problem-solving skills during the engineering process.

Materials

- Empty plastic water bottles (1-4 per group) with the bottoms cut off
- Various materials that can be used for filtration (sand, gravel, activated charcoal, coffee filters, cotton balls, fine mesh fabric, paper towels)
- Dirty water samples (mix small amount of coffee grounds in water ahead of time)
- Pitchers or containers for dirty water
- Containers for clean water
- Funnel
- Measuring cups or spoons
- Markers or labels
- Printed student instructions and response sheets (per group)

Design a Water Filter

Introduction

Begin by discussing the importance of clean and safe drinking water. Ask students to share their knowledge and experiences with water filtration. Some students may have water filters attached to their faucets or refrigerators at home, or their families may use a filtration pitcher.

Discuss common filtration materials such as sand, gravel, activated charcoal, and fabric filters. Some students may be familiar with coffee filters. It is possible that some students may be familiar with aquarium filters used in fish tanks.

The Challenge

Let the students know that today they will design their own water filters using materials of their choice.

Show your students the "dirty" water prepared earlier. Challenge them to design a filter that can make this water appear clear.

Remind students that when doing science or engineering experiments, we never drink any solution, even if it appears clear. We can not tell what is in a fluid by looking at it.

Encourage the students to experiment with different designs and configurations. They will try three different combinations of materials and then come up with a final water filter design to share with the class.

Demonstrate pouring the water through an empty bottle and into a bowl below. Remind students to pour slowly and carefully.

Design a Water Filter

Group Work: Phase 1 (15 min)

- Divide students into small groups or pairs and distribute the empty plastic water bottles.

- Instruct students to brainstorm and sketch their design ideas for the water filtration instrument.

- Encourage them to think about the materials they will use and how the filtration process will work.

- Assist students in identifying the filtration materials they will need and help them gather the necessary supplies.

Testing (10 min)

Encourage the groups to create at least three different designs. If you have enough water bottles, they can use a fresh bottle for each design. If not, they can empty their bottle out after trying each one.

Guide students with questions such as "What is working?" "Have you tried adding another layer?" "What if you use the same materials, but in a different order?"

Students record their designs on their response sheets and write down their thoughts on the student response sheet.

Have the groups combine features of their different designs to create their final, best design configuration to share with the rest of the class.

Design a Water Filter

Class Discussion (15 min)

- Bring the class back together to share and discuss.
- Discuss the design process with the class. Engineers try different solutions to engineering problems and test those solutions in order to come up with improved designs.
- Have groups share their best designs and talk about what worked for them and what didn't work.
- Allow other groups to comment or ask questions.
- Ask guiding questions to help student reflect on their designs:
    - How did you decide on the design of your water filter?
    - What factors did you consider?
    - What was the most challenging aspect of building your filter? Why?
    - Did you encounter any problems or unexpected issues during the design process? How did you handle those problems?
    - What materials did the best job of filtering the water?
    - What changes did you make to improve your initial designs?
    - How did working in a group impact the design and evaluation process? What were the advantages and challenges of collaborating on this project?

Design a Water Filter

Optional: Group Work: Phase 2

If you have enough time, you can allow small groups to use their new knowledge to design one more water filter.

If you have limited time, you can ask the students what improvements or modifications they would make if they were to build the filter again based on what they learned from the other groups in the class.

Conclusion (5 minutes)

Recap the key concepts learned during the activity, emphasizing the importance of using multiple materials to filter water.

Go over the engineering design process steps of discussion, design, testing, and redesign.

Discuss the potential real-world applications for water filtration.

Point out books in the classroom or school library that relate to engineering, water quality, and other related topics.

Collect the student response sheets.

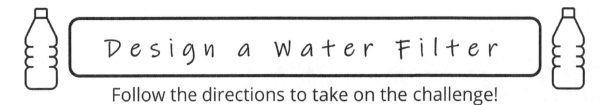

Follow the directions to take on the challenge!

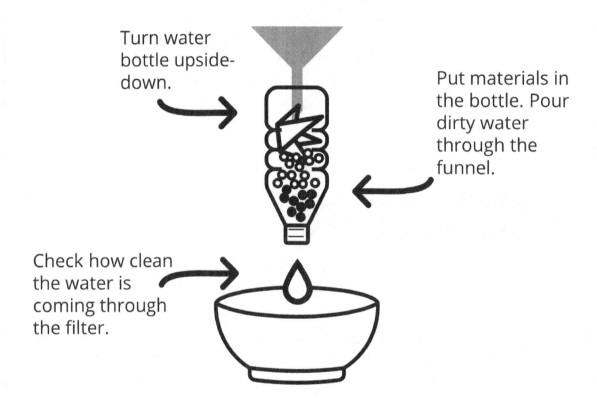

Turn water bottle upside-down.

Put materials in the bottle. Pour dirty water through the funnel.

Check how clean the water is coming through the filter.

As a group, you will build several water filters using various materials.

1. Discuss how to build your water filter.

2. Try three different filters and see how well they filter the water. Draw your designs and write down their details on your response sheet.

3. Discuss what you have learned from your three initial designs.

4. Decide upon your final design using what you have learned. Build your final design. Draw and note details of your final design.

5. Write about what configuration worked best and why.

6. Prepare to share your design with the class!

Names: _____

Design a Water Filter

Follow the directions to take on the challenge!

Design 1	Design 2	Design 3

Materials: _____   Materials: _____   Materials: _____

Final Design

Materials:

_____

What materials worked best?
In what order?

_____

_____

_____

_____

_____

_____

_____

Design a Water Filter

Extension Activities

- Repeat the activity, but instead of "dirty water" made with coffee grounds, try other impurities such as food coloring, orange juice, or a smoothie. What is filtered and what is not?

- Challenge students to research how people filter water in survival situations, such as living in the wilderness.

- Explore water quality issues in your local area and how they are being addressed.

- Try other filter materials such as:
    - Plain paper
    - Tissue paper
    - Different types of cloth
    - Plastic beads

- Take a field trip to a water treatment plant.

- Invite a guest speaker that is an environmental engineer, civil engineer, or water treatment plant employee to discuss how drinking water is treated in your community.

- View the National Institute of Environmental Health Sciences video about water treatment:
  kids.niehs.nih.gov/topics/pollution/water/treatment

- View the Reading Rainbow video about water treatment:
  thekidshouldseethis.com/post/explore-wastewater-treatment-with-levar-burton-reading-rainbow

Design a Water Filter

Resources

- For teacher inspiration, check out this TED Talk: www.ted.com/talks/michael_pritchard_how_to_make_filthy_ water_drinkable

- Students may enjoy watching the TED-Ed video: "Are We Running Out of Clean Water?"

- Read or provide some of the following books for your class to explore:

  - A Long Walk to Water by Linda Sue Park

  - National Geographic Kids - Water!: Why Every Drop Counts and How You Can Start Making Waves to Protect It by Lisa M. Gerry

  - Zoey and Sassafras: Merhorses and Bubbles by Asia Citro

  - DK The Survival Handbook by Colin Towell

  - A Child's Introduction to the Environment: The Air, Earth, and Sea Around Us by Michael Driscoll and Dennis Driscoll

  - The Everything Kids' Environment Book by Sheri Amsel

  - Poisoned Water: How the Citizens of Flint, Michigan, Fought for Their Lives and Warned the Nation by Candy J. Cooper and Marc Aronson

The Perfect Play Dough

Perfect Play Dough

Lesson

Perfect Play Dough: Exploring Material Engineering

Objectives

Students will:
- Explore material engineering through a hands-on activity involving making play dough
- Experiment in small groups with different materials and amounts of materials to find the best combinations
- Apply the engineering design principles to test, discuss, evaluate, and redesign their recipes

Materials

- Flour
- Salt
- Cream of Tartar
- Water
- Oil
- Measuring cups & spoons
- Mixing bowls
- Student instructions and response sheets

Vocabulary

- Latin root: "mater"
  - Material
- Components
- Ratio
- Engineering design

Perfect Play Dough

Introduction

Begin by asking students if they know the Latin root "mater." If not, give them some words that include this root such as: maternal, matriarch, and maternity. Lead the discussion to help them discover that "mater" means "mother."

You may have the class brainstorm more words that contain the root "mater."

Mention the vocabulary word **material**. Explain that material is what something is made of. Material engineers work with various materials to make things. Explain that the word material comes from the root "mater" as materials are the source of objects, just as mothers are the source of people and animals.

The Challenge

Let the students know that today they will make play dough out of various **materials**.

They will use flour, water, oil, cream of tartar, and salt to make dough. They should measure carefully and make note of how much of each ingredient they use. Explain that the proteins in the flour interact with water to become a stretchy dough. The salt helps preserve the dough and makes it smoother and elastic. The cream of tartar and oil make the dough softer.

Groups will be trying to make the best play dough using different **ratios** of these materials. Explain that ratios is how much there is of one thing compared to another.

Encourage the students to experiment with different amounts of the various materials to see how that affects the dough.

Perfect Play Dough

Group Work: Phase 1 (15 min)

- Divide students into small groups of 3-4 people.
- Distribute the materials, measuring cups and spoons to each group.
- Distribute the student response pages and ask students to record their initial designs in the top section.
- Have students note the consistency of each dough recipe.
- Circulate among the groups to provide guidance, answer questions, and facilitate discussions about the designs.

Testing (10 min)

Encourage the groups to create at least three different recipes with different ratios of components. Students should assess their playdough on how easy it is to use. They can assess its elasticity (how well it stretches), strength for building, and softness.

Students note the measurements of each material in their designs on their response sheets and record their findings.

Have the groups combine features of their trial recipes to create their final, best design to share with the rest of the class.

Circulate among the groups to help facilitate their discussions and decision process.

Perfect Play Dough

Class Discussion (15 min)

- Bring the class back together to share and discuss.
- Discuss the design process with the class. Engineers try different solutions to engineering problems and test those solutions in order to come up with improved designs.
- Ask groups to share their observations, discuss which ratios produced the best play dough, and explain their reasoning.
- Allow other groups to comment or ask questions.
- Ask guiding questions to help student reflect on their designs:
  - How did you decide how much of each component to add to your dough?
  - What was the most challenging aspect of creating your play dough? Why?
  - Did you encounter any problems or unexpected issues during the process? How did you handle those problems?
  - What combination of components made the best play dough?
  - What changes did you make to improve your initial designs?

Perfect Play Dough

Optional: Group Work: Phase 2

If you have enough time, you can allow small groups to use their new knowledge to design one more batch of play dough.

If you have limited time, you can ask the students what improvements or modifications they would make if they were to make playdough again based on what they learned from the other groups in the class.

Conclusion (5 minutes)

Recap the key concepts learned during the activity, emphasizing the importance of the properties of materials.

Go over the engineering design process steps of discussion, design, testing, and redesign.

Encourage students to think about how materials have various properties such as softness, strength, and elasticity.

Point out books in the classroom or school library that relate to engineering, materials, and other related topics.

Review the Latin root "mater" and the vocabulary word "material."

Collect the student response sheets.

Perfect Play Dough

Follow the directions to take on the challenge!

As a group, you will create your own play dough using various materials such as flour, salt, water, and oil.

1. Discuss how much of each ingredient you might need. Remember that you want your play dough to be strong enough to hold its shape, but still stretchy and soft.

2. Measure out your ingredients carefully for your first batch of dough. Stir or knead with your hands.

3. Write down the measurements and note the properties of your first batch of play dough on your response sheet.

4. Talk about what you might want to change for your next batch.

5. Try two more batches. Remember to write down the measurements and properties.

6. Discuss what you have learned from your three initial designs.

7. Decide upon your final design using what you have learned.

8. Mix your final design.

9. Note the measurements and properties of your final batch.

10. Prepare to share your final design with the class!

Names: _____

Perfect Play Dough

Follow the directions to take on the challenge!

Design 1

Flour: _____

Salt: _____

Cream of Tartar: _____

Water: _____

Oil: _____

Properties:_____

_____

Design 2

Flour: _____

Salt: _____

Cream of Tartar: _____

Water: _____

Oil: _____

Properties:_____

_____

Design 3

Flour: _____

Salt: _____

Cream of Tartar: _____

Water: _____

Oil: _____

Properties:_____

_____

Final Design

Flour: _____

Salt: _____

Cream of Tartar: _____

Water: _____

Oil: _____

Properties:_____

_____

_____

What combination of materials worked best? Why?

_____

_____

_____

_____

_____

_____

_____

Perfect Play Dough

Extension Activities

- Repeat the activity with the same ingredients, but instead of making play dough, try different combinations of components to make an adhesive like paste.

- Use the play dough to make different shapes or objects.

- Explore different ways to color the play dough such as food coloring, watercolor paint, drink mix, natural dyes, ink, or glitter.

- Try making dough with other materials such as:
  - Lemon juice
  - Different kinds of flour
  - Baking soda
  - Shortening

- Take a field trip to a factory that mixes materials

- Take a field trip to a dentist office to see materials being mixed for fillings and crown adhesive

- Invite a guest speaker that is an artist, baker, material engineer, chemical engineer, or dental hygienist to discuss combining substances to make new materials.

- Students may enjoy watching play dough animations and trying some of their own.

Perfect Play Dough

Resources

- For teacher inspiration, check out this TED Talk: www.ted.com/talks/annmarie_thomas_hands_on_science_ with_squishy_circuits

- Browse the Guinness Book of World Records account of a giant mosaic of play dough in Mexico: www.guinnessworldrecords.com/news/2016/9/play-doh-mexico-creates-a-beautiful-artistic-record-for-60th-anniversary-445382

- Read or provide some of the following books for your class to explore:

  - Make - Edible Inventions: Cooking Hacks and Yummy Recipes You Can Build, Mix, Bake, and Grow by Kathy Ceceri

  - Exploring Kitchen Science: 30+ Edible Experiments and Kitchen Activities by The Exploratorium

  - Good Housekeeping – Kids Bake! by Susan Westmoreland

  - Frosting and Friendship by Lisa Shroeder

  - A Single Shard by Linda Sue Park

  - Clay Lab for Kids: 52 Projects to Make, Model, and Mold with Air-Dry, Polymer, and Homemade Clay by Cassie Stephens

Bubbles and Wands

Bubbles and Wands

Lesson

Bubbles and Wands: Material Engineering and Product Design

Objectives

Students will:

- Explore the engineering design process by experimenting with different recipes for bubble solutions and designing various bubble wands
- Work collaboratively in small groups to test and evaluate different combinations of recipes and wand designs
- Engage in a class discussion to share their findings, analyze results, and draw conclusions
- Develop critical thinking, problem-solving, and communication skills through hands-on experimentation and reflection

Materials

- Dish soap
- Water
- Glycerin
- Sugar
- Corn syrup
- Detergent
- Mixing containers
- Measuring cups & spoons
- Various materials for wands (pipe cleaners, wire, straws, beads, string, etc.)
- Timers
- Student instructions and response sheets

Vocabulary

- Solution
- Surface tension
- Materials
- Components
- Ratio
- Engineering design

Bubbles and Wands

Introduction

Begin by asking students if they know the word "solution." Some students may be familiar with bubble solution or contact lens solution. Explain that a **solution** is a special mixture where something is dissolved in another substance such as water.

The Challenge

Explain that today they will be making a bubble solution with various ingredients and making bubble wands with different materials.

Bubble solution is often made with ingredients such as soap, water, glycerin, sugar, corn syrup, and detergent in different amounts. Students will be trying to make the best bubble recipe using different **ratios** of these materials. Explain that a ratio is how much there is of one thing compared to another.

Point out that plain water does not make very fun bubbles, because the **surface tension** of water is too high. This means the water molecules want to stick together rather than form big bubbles. But other ingredients like soap and glycerin can lower the surface tension, allowing big bubbles to form. Discuss some of the properties to look for in good bubbles such as being big, strong, and long-lasting.

Encourage the students to experiment with different amounts of the various materials to see how that affects the bubbles.

Bubbles and Wands

Group Work: Phase 1 (15 min)

- Divide students into small groups of 3-4 people.

- Distribute the materials, supplies, measuring cups and spoons, timers, and mixing containers to each group.

- Distribute the student response pages and ask students to record their initial designs in the top section.

- Have students note the properties of their bubbles.

- Circulate among the groups to provide guidance, answer questions, and facilitate discussions about the designs.

Testing (10 min)

Encourage the groups to create at least three different recipes with different ratios of components. Students should assess the properties of their bubbles and time how long they last. They should note this information on their response sheets and record their findings.

The students can try different bubble wand designs for each of their bubble solutions and see how the wand shape and materials affect their bubbles.

Have the groups combine features of their trial recipes and wands to create their final, best design to share with the rest of the class.

Circulate among the groups to help facilitate their discussions and decision process.

Bubbles and Wands

Class Discussion (15 min)

- Bring the class back together to share and discuss.
- Discuss the design process with the class. Engineers try different solutions to engineering problems and test those solutions in order to come up with improved designs.
- Ask groups to share their observations, discuss which ratios produced the best bubble solution, and talk about their wand designs.
- Allow other groups to comment or ask questions.
- Ask guiding questions to help student reflect on their designs:
    - How did you decide how much of each component to add to your solution?
    - What was the most challenging aspect of creating your bubble solution and wands? Why?
    - Did you encounter any problems or unexpected issues during the process? How did you handle those problems?
    - What combination of components made the best bubble solution?
    - What changes did you make to improve your initial designs?

Optional: Group Work: Phase 2

If you have enough time, you can allow small groups to use their new knowledge to design one more batch of bubble solution.

If you have limited time, you can ask the students what improvements or modifications they would make if they were to make bubbles again based on what they learned from the other groups in the class.

Conclusion (5 minutes)

Recap the key concepts learned during the activity, emphasizing the importance of the engineering design process steps of discussion, design, testing, and redesign.

Encourage students to think about how the ratio of ingredients affected their bubbles.

Point out books in the classroom or school library that relate to engineering, materials, and other related topics.

Review the vocabulary words "solution" and "surface tension."

Collect the student response sheets.

Bubbles and Wands

Follow the directions to take on the challenge!

As a group, you will create your own bubble solution using various materials such as water, soap, glycerin, and sugar.

1. Discuss how much of each ingredient you might need. Remember that you want your bubbles to be big and last a long time.

2. Measure out your ingredients carefully for your first batch of bubble solution. Write down the measurements.

3. Note the properties of your first bubbles on your response sheet, including how many seconds they lasted before popping.

4. Talk about what you might want to change for your next batch.

5. Try two more batches. Remember to write down the measurements and properties.

6. Discuss what you have learned from your three initial designs.

7. Decide upon your final design using what you have learned.

8. Mix your final design.

9. Note the measurements and properties of your final batch.

10. Prepare to share your final design with the class!

Student Response Sheet

Names: _____

Bubbles and Wands

Follow the directions to take on the challenge!

Design 1

Water: _____

Soap: _____

Glycerin: _____

Sugar: _____

Other: _____

Size: big   medium   small

Time: _____

Design 2

Water: _____

Soap: _____

Glycerin: _____

Sugar: _____

Other: _____

Size: big   medium   small

Time: _____

Design 3

Water: _____

Soap: _____

Glycerin: _____

Sugar: _____

Other: _____

Size: big   medium   small

Time: _____

Final Design

Water: _____

Soap: _____

Glycerin: _____

Sugar: _____

Other: _____

Size: big   medium   small

Time: _____

What combination of materials worked best? Why?

_____

_____

_____

_____

_____

_____

_____

Bubbles and Wands

Extension Activities

- Calculate the ratios of soap to water for the best bubble solutions.
- Repeat the activity with the same ingredients, but instead of making bubble solution, try different combinations of components to make a play foam.
- See which team can make the biggest bubble.
- Explore different ways to color the bubble solution such as food coloring, watercolor paint, or drink mix.
- Try making bubbles with other materials such as:
    - Shampoo
    - Body wash
    - Honey
    - Bottled water
- Take a field trip to a factory that mixes materials
- Invite a guest speaker that is a scientist, material engineer, or chemical engineer to discuss combining substances to make new materials.
- Students may enjoy learning about the Guinness Book of World Records account of the largest free floating soap bubble, which was over 3,000 cubic feet! www.guinnessworldrecords.com/world-records/largest-free-floating-soap-bubble

Bubbles and Wands

Resources

- For teacher inspiration, check out this TED Talk: www.ted.com/talks/li_wei_tan_the_fascinating_science_of_bubbles_from_soap_to_champagne

- Read or provide some of the following books for your class to explore:
    - Fire Bubbles and Exploding Toothpaste: More Unforgettable Experiments that Make Science Fun by Steve Spangler
    - Fizz, Bubble, & Flash by Anita Brandolini
    - DK Eyewitness Books – Chemistry: Discover the Amazing Effect Chemistry Has on Every Part of Our Lives by Ann Newmark
    - The Everything Kids Science Experiments Book by Tom Robinson
    - The Cartoon Guide to Chemistry by Larry Gonick and Craig Criddle
    - Janice VanCleave's Chemistry for Every Kid: 101 Easy Experiments that Really Work by Janice VanCleave

Suspension Bridge

Suspension Bridge

Lesson

Build a Suspension Bridge: Exploring Engineering Design

Objectives

Students will:
- Learn about suspension bridges, their designs, and how they distribute weight.
- Work collaboratively in a small group.
- Design and test a bridge to span a distance and hold a load.
- Apply the engineering design principles to test, discuss, evaluate, and redesign their structures.

Materials

- Cardboard & other materials
- Two chairs or desks
- Weights (e.g. wooden blocks)
- Student instructions and response sheets (per group)
- String or yarn
- Masking tape
- Measuring tape

Vocabulary

- Suspension
- Load
- Span
- Anchor
- Construct
- Engineering design

Suspension Bridge

Introduction

Begin by tying a string around a weight such as a block and stretch the string over the back of a chair. Demonstrate how this changes the direction of the force so when you pull the string down, the weight goes up.

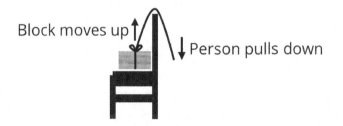

Block moves up ↑   ↓ Person pulls down

The Challenge

Let the students know that there is a kind of bridge that takes advantage of this. It is called a **suspension bridge** and the surface of the bridge is held up by cables that are held down on the ground.

Show your students some images of suspension bridges online or in books (see the resources section of this lesson for book ideas). Point out the towers, deck, cables and anchors.

Explain to the students that they will be making suspension bridges using cardboard, string, and other materials. Their bridges will **span** the gap between two chairs. Their bridges will hold a **load** of heavy blocks to show their strength.

Encourage the students to experiment with different designs and configurations.

Suspension Bridge

Group Work: Phase 1 (10 min)

- Divide students into small groups of 3-4 people.

- Distribute the materials to each group.

- Distribute the student response pages and ask students to draw some of their initial designs in the top section.

- Instruct students to plan and construct their bridges, measuring the span and how much load it can hold.

- Circulate among the groups to provide guidance, answer questions, and facilitate discussions about the designs.

Testing (15 min)

Encourage the groups to create at least three different designs and assess their spans and the loads they can hold. What configuration spans the greatest distance? What design holds the greatest load?

Students record the details on their response sheets.

Have the groups combine features of their different designs to create their final, best design configuration to share with the rest of the class.

Circulate among the groups to help facilitate their discussions and decision process.

Have students draw, measure, and note the details about their final structures on the student response sheet.

Suspension Bridge

Class Discussion (15 min)

- Bring the class back together to share and discuss.
- Discuss the design process with the class. Engineers try different solutions to engineering problems and test those solutions in order to come up with improved designs.
- Have groups share their best designs and talk about what worked for them and what didn't work.
- Allow other groups to comment or ask questions.
- Ask guiding questions to help student reflect on their designs:
    - How did you decide on the design of your bridge?
    - What factors did you consider?
    - What was the most challenging aspect of building your bridge? Why?
    - Did you encounter any problems or unexpected issues during the construction process? How did you handle those problems?
    - How did you construct your towers?
    - What changes did you make to improve your initial designs?
    - How did working in a group impact the design and evaluation process? What were the advantages and challenges of collaborating on this project?

Optional: Group Work: Phase 2

If you have enough time, you can allow small groups to use their new knowledge to design one more suspension bridge.

If you have limited time, you can ask the students what improvements or modifications they would make if they were to build the bridge again based on what they learned from the other groups in the class.

Conclusion (5 minutes)

Recap the key concepts learned during the activity, emphasizing how the direction of forces can be changed.

Go over the engineering design process steps of discussion, design, testing, and redesign.

Encourage students to think about how engineering principles impact the design and stability of various bridges.

Point out books in the classroom or school library that relate to engineering, bridges, and other related topics.

Review the vocabulary words: "suspension," "span," and "load."

Collect the student response sheets.

Suspension Bridge

Build a suspension bridge that spans across two desks!

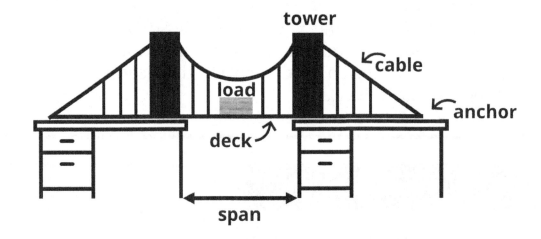

As a group, you will build a suspension bridge. Try different designs to see what works best!

1. Build a deck that spans the distance across two desks. Measure the span and note it in your response sheet.

2. Create two towers and attach a cable made of string across them, extending to the left and right of the deck edges. Anchor the ends of the string well with tape.

3. Connect the deck to the cables with more pieces of string.

4. Try adding wooden blocks (a load) to the middle of the bridge. How many can you add before the bridge starts to fail? Note the number on your response sheet.

5. Make some changes and see how that affects your bridge. For example, you could move the towers closer or farther away. Does this change what load your bridge can hold?

6. Create three different designs and use what you have learned to create one more, final design.

Names: _____

Suspension Bridge

Follow the directions to take on the challenge!

Design 1

Span: _____

Load: _____

Design 2

Span: _____

Load: _____

Design 3

Span: _____

Load: _____

Final Design

Span: _____

Load: _____

What configuration worked best? Why?

_____

_____

_____

_____

_____

_____

_____

Suspension Bridge

Extension Activities

- Have your students partner up facing each other and hold hands. Have them lean back to feel a tension force, then lean towards each other to feel a compression force. In suspension bridges, the towers are under compression and the cables are under tension forces.

- Make similar bridges without the cables and see which type can carry a load over a larger span.

- Try building with other materials such as:
    - Interlocking plastic blocks
    - Straws
    - Popsicle sticks
    - Dental floss
    - Yarm

- Take a field trip to see a suspension bridge in person.

- Invite a guest speaker that is an architect, structural engineer, civil engineer, or builder to discuss building bridges.

- Your students may be interested in learning about the suspension grass rope bridges made by the Quechua (Inca) that were built to span rivers and canyons in Peru.

Suspension Bridge

Resources

- For teacher inspiration, check out this TED Talk: "Bridges Should Be Beautiful"
- Students may enjoy watching the TED-Ed video: "Building the Impossible: Golden Gate Bridge"
- Read or provide some of the following books for your class to explore:
    - Bridges! Amazing Structures by Carol Johmann and Elizabeth Rieth
    - Bridges: A History of the World's Most Spectacular Spans by Judith Dupre
    - The Great Bridge: The Epic Story of the Building of the Brooklyn Bridge by David McCullough. (This book is aimed at adults, but still may be appealing to a student who is highly interested in this topic)
    - The Golden Gate Bridge by Jeffrey Zuehlke
    - How Emily Saved the Bridge: The Story of Emily Warren Roebling and the Building of the Brooklyn Bridge by Frieda Wishinsky

Basketball Game

Basketball Game

Lesson

Build a Mini Basketball Game: Fun with Engineering Design

Objectives

Students will:
- Design a mini basketball game made with common household materials.
- Learn the concept of a fulcrum.
- Work collaboratively in a small group.
- Apply the engineering design principles to test, discuss, evaluate, and redesign their creations.

Materials

- Things that can be used as balls (balls, plastic eggs, mini erasers)
- Things that can be used as hoops (bracelets, canning jar rings)
- Things that can be used a fulcrum (blocks, toilet paper tubes)
- Plastic spoons
- A chair or box
- Masking tape
- Student instructions and response sheets

Vocabulary

- Fulcrum
- Iteration
- Construct
- Engineering design

Basketball Game

Introduction

Begin by telling the students that they will be working in groups to construct mini basketball games. If they are not already familiar, you may want to introduce them to the concept of a **fulcrum** and show them how pushing down on one side makes the other side go up. (To do this you could place a ruler over a wooden block or similar object)

Emphasize that we will be building things, taking them apart, and rebuilding them. We will test our designs and use the results to help us improve our creations. This is called design **iteration**.

The Challenge

Talk to the students about how engineers use materials that are available and tinker to find something that works to solve a problem. Unlike some science labs or kits that they have used in the past, in this lesson they can use any material available and switch out materials as needed. If they want to make this again at home, they can use totally different materials to create a new design.

Explain that the plastic spoon on a fulcrum will launch the ball when the push down on the handle. It is up to them to figure out the best way to attach components, how far apart to place things, and what materials to use. They will find out by trying different things and making changes to their designs as needed.

Encourage the students to experiment with different designs and configurations to find something that works.

Basketball Game

Group Work: Phase 1 (10 min)

- Divide students into small groups of 3-4 people.

- Distribute the materials to each group.

- Distribute the student response pages and ask students to draw some of their initial designs in the top section.

- Instruct students to plan and construct their games, then test them out.

- Circulate among the groups to provide guidance, answer questions, and facilitate discussions about the designs.

Testing (15 min)

Encourage the groups to create at least three different designs and test them. Is the launcher close enough to the hoop? Would a different ball work better? Guide them with questions and encourage them to try lots of different things.

Students record the details of their games on their response sheets.

Have the groups combine features of their different designs to create their final, best design configuration to share with the rest of the class.

Circulate among the groups to help facilitate their discussions and decision process.

Have students draw and note the details about their final structures on the student response sheet.

Basketball Game

Class Discussion (15 min)

- Bring the class back together to share and discuss.
- Discuss the design process with the class. Engineers try different solutions to engineering problems and test those solutions in order to come up with improved designs.
- Have groups share their best designs and talk about what worked for them and what didn't work.
- Allow other groups to comment or ask questions.
- Ask guiding questions to help student reflect on their designs:
  - What did you try first?
  - What changes did you make?
  - What was the most challenging aspect of constructing your game? Why?
  - Did you encounter any problems or unexpected issues during the construction process? How did you handle those problems?
  - What did you learn from the process?
  - How did working in a group impact the design and evaluation process? What were the advantages and challenges of collaborating on this project?

Basketball Game

Optional: Group Work: Phase 2

If you have enough time, you can allow small groups to use their new knowledge to design one more mini basketball game.

If you have limited time, you can ask the students what improvements or modifications they would make if they were to build the game again based on what they learned from the other groups in the class.

Conclusion (5 minutes)

Recap the key concepts learned during the activity, emphasizing the engineering design process steps of discussion, design, testing, and redesign.

Encourage students to think about how they were able to improve their designs through trying different things.

Point out books in the classroom or school library that relate to engineering, physics, and other related topics.

Review the vocabulary words: "iteration" and "fulcrum."

Collect the student response sheets.

Basketball Game

Build a mini basketball game!

Ideas for the ball	Ideas for the hoop	Ideas for the fulcrum
• Toy ball • Plastic egg • Crumpled paper • Cotton ball • Mini eraser • Marsh-mallow	• Bangle bracelet • Canning jar ring • Embroidery hoop • Cookie cutter	• Wooden block  • Paper towel tube • Eraser • Ruler • A thick marker

As a group, you will build a mini basketball game. Try different designs to see what works best!

1. Attach something to serve as the hoop.

2. Make a launcher by putting the plastic spoon over something that serves as the fulcrum.

3. Anchor the fulcrum and spoon.

4. Place the ball on the spoon. Try launching it so that it goes through the hoop. Change materials, placements, and configurations until you find one that works.

5. Draw your first three attempts and note what changes you made.

6. Use what you have learned to create one more, final design. Draw it on your response sheet and be prepared to share it with the class.

Student Response Sheet

Names: _____

Basketball Game

Follow the directions to take on the challenge!

Design 1

Design 2

What we changed:

_____

_____

Design 3

What we changed:

_____

_____

Final Design

What we changed:

_____

_____

_____

What configuration worked best? Why?

_____

_____

_____

_____

_____

_____

_____

Basketball Game

Extension Activities

- Discuss other examples of how fulcrums are used for levers in the real world, such as teeter-totters, crowbars, and wheelbarrows.

- Extend the discussion to simple machines in general as part of a larger unit.

- Make other mini games such as table tennis, soccer, and so on.

- Make a larger sized basketball game out on the playground with a launcher big enough for a basketball.

- Take a field trip to a design firm and learn about how new things are invented and designed.

- Start a tinkering lab where kids can make new things out of recycled and found materials.

- Invite a guest speaker that is an inventor, product engineer, mechanical engineer, or physicist to discuss the design process.

- Your students may be interested in seeing videos of giant catapults and trebuchets. This is a great connection to a history lesson if you are studying ancient times or the middle ages.

Basketball Game

- For teacher inspiration, check out this TED Talk: www.ted.com/talks/gever_tulley_life_lessons_through_tinkering

- Students may enjoy watching the TED-Ed video: ed.ted.com/lessons/the-mighty-mathematics-of-the-lever-andy-peterson-and-zack-patterson

- Read or provide some of the following books for your class to explore:
  - The Way Things Work by David Macaulay
  - Super Simple Physics by DK Smithsonian
  - Simple Machines by D.J. Ward
  - Make Fun!: Make Your Own Toys, Games, and Amusements by Bob Knetzger
  - Tinkering: Kids Learn by Making Stuff by Curt Gabrielson
  - It's a Numbers Game! Basketball: The Math Behind the Perfect Bounce Pass, the Buzzer-beating Bank Shot, and So Much More! By James Buckley Jr.
  - The Magnificent Makers Series by Theanne Griffith
  - Weird Little Robots by Carolyn Crimi
  - Maya and the Robot by Eve L. Ewing

Make a Wind Chime

Make a Wind Chime

Lesson

Make a Wind Chime Using the Engineering Design Process

Objectives

Students will:
- Design a wind chime made with common household materials.
- Learn the concept of pitch.
- Work collaboratively in a small group.
- Apply the engineering design principles to test, discuss, evaluate, and redesign their creations.

Materials

Things that can be used for the top:
- Sticks
- Canning jar rings
- Small colanders
- Clothing hangers
- Small flower pots
- String or yarn

Things that make sound:
- Keys
- Beads
- Bottle caps
- Shells
- Spoons
- Bells

Vocabulary

- Pitch
- Vibration
- Iteration
- Engineering design

Make a Wind Chime

Introduction

Begin by telling the students that they will be working in groups to make wind chimes. You may show them an example of a wind chime or a short video online if they are not familiar with them.

Demonstrate how striking a larger object results in a lower **pitch** than a smaller object. You can do this buy attaching a large metal object (e.g. a spoon) to a string and striking it, then doing the same with a small object (e.g. a key). The pitch is lower for the larger object because it has a slower **vibration**.

Emphasize that we will be building things, taking them apart, and rebuilding them. We will test our designs and use the results to help us improve our creations. This is called design **iteration**.

The Challenge

Talk to the students about how engineers use materials that are available and tinker to find something that works to solve a problem. Unlike some science labs or kits that they have used in the past, in this lesson they can use any material available and switch out materials as needed. If they want to make this again at home, they can use totally different materials to create a new design.

Explain that they with start by selecting something for the top of the wind chime. They will then use string to attach items that make sound. When those items move in the wind, they strike each other, causing them to vibrate and make sound. If they want high-pitched sounds, they should select smaller items. If they want low-pitched sounds, they should select larger items.

Encourage the students to experiment with different designs and configurations to find something that they like best.

Make a Wind Chime

Group Work: Phase 1 (10 min)

- Divide students into small groups of 3-4 people.

- Distribute the materials to each group.

- Distribute the student response pages and ask students to draw some of their initial designs in the top section.

- Instruct students to plan and construct their wind chimes, then test them out. (If you have a table or room fan, allow students to use it for testing!)

- Circulate among the groups to provide guidance, answer questions, and facilitate discussions about the designs.

Testing (15 min)

Encourage the groups to create at least three different designs and test them. Does their wind chime make sound? Do they like the pitch? Guide them with questions and encourage them to try lots of different things.

Students record the details of their wind chimes on their response sheets.

Have the groups combine features of their different designs to create their final, best design configuration to share with the rest of the class.

Circulate among the groups to help facilitate their discussions and decision process.

Have students draw and note the details about their final designs on the student response sheet.

Make a Wind Chime

Class Discussion (15 min)

- Bring the class back together to share and discuss.
- Discuss the design process with the class. Engineers try different solutions to engineering problems and test those solutions in order to come up with improved designs.
- Have groups share their best designs and talk about what worked for them and what didn't work.
- Allow other groups to comment or ask questions.
- Ask guiding questions to help student reflect on their designs:
    - What did you try first?
    - What changes did you make?
    - What was the most challenging aspect of constructing your wind chime? Why?
    - Did you encounter any problems or unexpected issues during the construction process? How did you handle those problems?
    - What did you learn from the process?
    - How did working in a group impact the design and evaluation process? What were the advantages and challenges of collaborating on this project?

Make a Wind Chime

Optional: Group Work: Phase 2

If you have enough time, you can allow small groups to use their new knowledge to design one more wind chime.

If you have limited time, you can ask the students what improvements or modifications they would make if they were to build the wind chime again based on what they learned from the other groups in the class.

Conclusion (5 minutes)

Recap the key concepts learned during the activity, emphasizing the engineering design process steps of discussion, design, testing, and redesign.

Encourage students to think about how they were able to improve their designs through trying different things.

Point out books in the classroom or school library that relate to music, physics, engineering, and other related topics.

Review the vocabulary words: "pitch" and "vibration."

Collect the student response sheets.

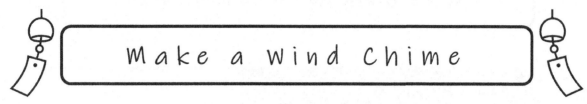

Make a Wind Chime

Make your own wind chime!

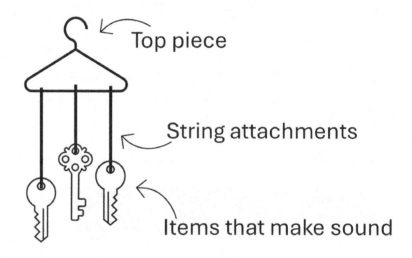

As a group, you will build a wind chime. Try different designs to see what works best!

1. Select something for the top.

2. Choose items that made sound.

3. Use string to attach the items to the top.

4. Move it gently or place it in front of a fan. How does it sound? Is the pitch too high or low? Change materials, placements, and configurations until you find one that you like best.

5. Draw your first three attempts and note what changes you made.

6. Use what you have learned to create one more, final design. Draw it on your response sheet and be prepared to share it with the class.

Student Response Sheet

Names: _____

Make a Wind Chime

Follow the directions to take on the challenge!

Design 1	Design 2	Design 3
	What we changed: _____ _____	What we changed: _____ _____

Final Design

What we changed:

_____

_____

_____

What configuration worked best? Why?

_____

_____

_____

_____

_____

_____

Make a Wind Chime

Extension Activities

- Research wind chimes from around the world. Discuss what they have in common and what is different between them.

- Discuss how the pitch of each bar on a xylophone is affected by the size.

- Discuss musical instruments in general and how their sizes affect their pitch ranges.

- Extend the activity to make more musical instruments such as flutes, guitars, and drums.

- Take a field trip to a music store and learn about different instruments and their sounds.

- Take a field trip to an orchestra concert and talk about how the sounds of the instruments compare.

- Start a tinkering lab where kids can make new things out of recycled and found materials.

- Invite a guest speaker that is an inventor, musician, engineer, or physicist to discuss sound and the design process.

- Your students may be interested in each making their own wind chime to keep. You can do this as a class project or assign it as an optional homework assignment.

- Challenge students to make their own instruments at home and bring them to share with the class.

Make a Wind Chime

- For teacher inspiration, check out this TED Talk: www.ted.com/talks/robert_gupta_between_music_and_medicine

- Students may enjoy watching the TED-Ed video: www.ted.com/talks/anita_collins_how_playing_an_instrument_benefits_your_brain

- Read or provide some of the following books for your class to explore:

    - Music and How It Works: The Complete Guide for Kids by DK

    - Turn It Up!: A Pitch Perfect History of Music that Rocked the World by National Geographic Kids

    - Musical Inventions: DIY Instruments to Toot, Tap, Crank, Strum, Pluck, and Switch On by Kathy Ceceri

    - Wind Chimes and Whirligigs by Renee Schwarz

    - Super Simple Physics: The Ultimate Bitesize Guide by DK

    - The Physics Book: Big Ideas Simply Explained by DK

    - Physical Science Energy: A True Book by Jacob Batchelor

D.I.Y.
Mini Golf

D.I.Y. Mini Golf

Lesson

D.I.Y. Minigolf: Project-Based Learning Engineering Design

Objectives

Students will:
- Design a minigolf course made with common household materials.
- Learn the concept of momentum.
- Work collaboratively in a small group.
- Apply the engineering design principles to test, discuss, evaluate, and redesign their creations.

Materials

- Small balls
- Wrapping paper tubes or
- Pool noodles or similar
- Cups
- Hoops
- Student instructions and response sheets
- Cardboard
- Masking tape
- Obstacles
- Plastic cones
- Various materials

Vocabulary

- Momentum
- Friction
- Construct
- Engineering design

D.I.Y. Mini Golf

Introduction

Begin by telling the students that they will be working in groups to construct a minigolf course. Ask students if they have tried minigolf or seen a course before. You may want to show them photos of a course if they have not seen one.

Introduce them to the concept of **momentum**. Momentum is a concept that describes how objects that are moving tend to stay moving, whereas objects at rest tend to stay at rest unless acted on by an external force.

Emphasize that we will be building things, taking them apart, and rebuilding them. We will test our designs and use the results to help us improve our creations. This is called design **iteration**.

The Challenge

Talk to the students about how the minigolf club puts a force on the ball. This changes the momentum of the ball and makes it move. The ball would keep going forever if it wasn't for air resistance and **friction**. Friction is the resistance the ball encounters while moving across the surface.

Explain that they will choose materials for the minigolf clubs, balls, goals, and obstacles. They want to balance making the minigolf course challenging but still able to be completed. They will try different materials and configurations to create a fun game.

Encourage the students to experiment with different designs and make many changes to find the design they like the best.

D.I.Y. Mini Golf

Group Work: Phase 1 (10 min)

- Divide students into small groups of 3-4 people.

- Distribute the materials to each group.

- Distribute the student response pages and ask students to draw some of their initial designs in the top section.

- Instruct students to plan and construct their courses, then test them out.

- Circulate among the groups to provide guidance, answer questions, and facilitate discussions about the designs.

Testing (15 min)

Encourage the groups to create at least three different designs and test them. Are they sometimes able to get the ball in the goal? Does the surface have enough friction? Or too much friction? Guide them with questions and encourage them to try lots of different things.

Students record the details of their games on their response sheets. They should then combine features of their different designs to create their final, best design configuration to share with the rest of the class.

Circulate among the groups to help facilitate their discussions and decision process.

Have students draw and note the details about their final structures on the student response sheet.

D.I.Y. Mini Golf

Class Discussion (15 min)

- Bring the class back together to share and discuss.
- Discuss the design process with the class. Engineers try different solutions to engineering problems and test those solutions in order to come up with improved designs.
- Have groups share their best designs and talk about what worked for them and what didn't work.
- Allow other groups to comment or ask questions.
- Ask guiding questions to help student reflect on their designs:
    - What did you try first?
    - What changes did you make?
    - What was the most challenging aspect of constructing your game? Why?
    - Did you encounter any problems or unexpected issues during the construction process? How did you handle those problems?
    - What did you learn from the process?
    - How did working in a group impact the design and evaluation process? What were the advantages and challenges of collaborating on this project?

D.I.Y. Mini Golf

Optional: Group Work: Phase 2

If you have enough time, you can allow small groups to use their new knowledge to improve their minigolf course.

If you have limited time, you can ask the students what improvements or modifications they would make if they were to build the course again based on what they learned from the other groups in the class.

Conclusion (5 minutes)

Recap the key concepts learned during the activity, emphasizing the engineering design process steps of discussion, design, testing, and redesign.

Encourage students to think about how they were able to improve their designs through trying different things.

Point out books in the classroom or school library that relate to golf, engineering, physics, and other related topics.

Review the vocabulary words: "momentum" and "friction."

Collect the student response sheets.

D.I.Y. Mini Golf

Build a minigolf game!

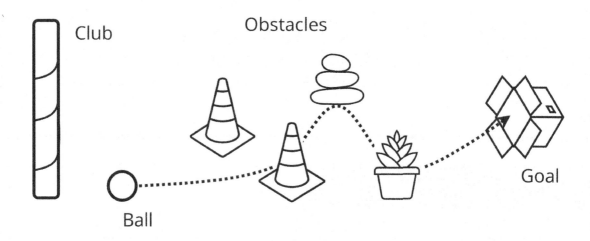

As a group, you will build a minigolf game. Try different designs to see what works best!

1. Choose a surface (blacktop, grass, cardboard, blanket, etc.)

2. Select something to serve as the club.

3. Select a ball.

4. Set up several obstacles and items for the ball to bounce off from.

5. Choose a goal such as a cup or empty box.

6. Try your game! Move things and try different materials.

7. Draw your first three attempts and note what changes you made.

8. Use what you have learned to create one more, final design. Draw it on your response sheet and be prepared to share it with the class.

Student Response Sheet

Names: _____

D.I.Y. Mini Golf

Follow the directions to take on the challenge!

Design 1	Design 2	Design 3
	What we changed: _____ _____	What we changed: _____ _____

Final Design

What we changed:

_____
_____
_____

What configuration worked best? Why?

_____
_____
_____
_____
_____
_____

D.I.Y. Mini Golf

Extension Activities

- Discuss the surfaces, obstacles, and goals that your students have seen at minigolf courses.

- Invite another class to come and try your minigolf course! If you class is "buddies" with another class, this is a great activity for kids to do together.

- Make other outdoor games such as bocce ball, cornhole, and ring toss.

- Take a field trip to a minigolf or golf course to see the real thing in action.

- Do more demonstrations of momentum, such as a rolling marble hitting a stationary marble.

- Invite a guest speaker that is an inventor, product engineer, mechanical engineer, or physicist to discuss momentum, friction, or the design process.

- Your students may be interested in seeing videos of Rube Goldberg machines, which often show the change of momentum when a moving object encounters a stationary object. You can view a video about the world's largest Rube Goldberg machine or learn how to make one.

D.I.Y. Mini Golf

- For teacher inspiration, check out this TED Talk: www.ted.com/talks/silvana_mejia_golf_the_closest_game_to_ explain_life
- Students may enjoy watching the TED-Ed video: "The Golf Ball That Made Golfers Too Good"
- Read or provide some of the following books for your class to explore:
  - The Kids Book of Golf by John Gordon
  - Forces Make Things Move by Kimberly Bradley
  - A Crash Course in Forces and Motion with Max Axiom, Super Scientist by Emily Beth Sohn
  - Investigating Forces and Motion: Physical Science by Jane Weir
  - Just Like Rube Goldberg: The Incredible True Story of the Man Behind the Machines by Sarah Aronson
  - Rube Goldberg and His Amazing Machines by Brandon T. Snider
  - Cardboard Box Engineering: Cool, Inventive Projects for Tinkerers, Makers & Future Scientists by Jonathan Adolph

D.I.Y. Arcade Games

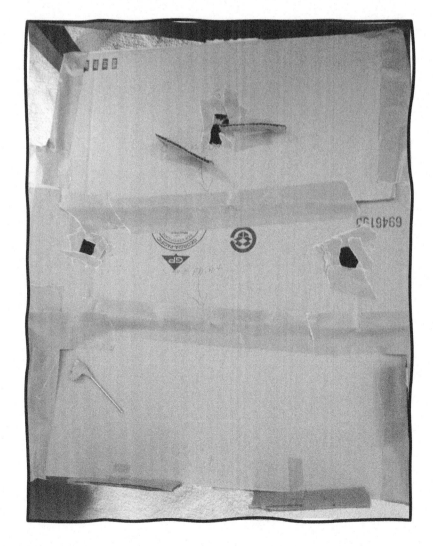

D.I.Y. Arcade

Lesson

D.I.Y. Arcade: Project-Based Learning Engineering Design

Objectives

Students will:
- Design arcade games made with common household materials.
- Learn the concept of gravity.
- Work collaboratively in a small group.
- Apply the engineering design principles to test, discuss, evaluate, and redesign their creations.

Materials

- Many large cardboard boxes
- Scissors
- Pencils
- Cups
- Rubber bands
- Student instructions and response sheets
- Twist ties
- Masking tape
- Balls
- Various other materials
- Tickets or prizes (optional)

Vocabulary

- Gravity
- Force
- Construct
- Engineering design

D.I.Y. Arcade

Introduction

Begin by telling the students that they will be working in groups to construct an arcade. Ask students if they have been to an arcade before. You may want to show them photos of classic arcade games (for example: skeeball, whack-a-mole, pinball, etc.) if they have not seen them before.

Discuss the concept of **gravity** as a **force** that pulls things down. Many of the traditional arcade games rely on gravity to work.

Emphasize that we will be building things, taking them apart, and rebuilding them. We will test our designs and use the results to help us improve our creations. This is called design **iteration**.

The Challenge

Talk to the students about how many arcade games begin with the player launching a ball upward. For example:
- Rolling a ball up a ramp in skeeball
- Hitting a ball up the board with a flipper in pinball
- Throwing a basketball up toward a hoop

Gravity then causes the ball to roll back down.

Explain that they will choose materials for the arcade games and try different configurations to make it work well. They want to balance making the game challenging but still able to be completed. They will try different materials and configurations to create a fun game.

Encourage the students to experiment with different designs and make many changes to find the design they like the best.

D.I.Y. Arcade

Group Work: Phase 1 (10 min)

- Divide students into small groups of 3-4 people.

- Distribute the materials to each group.

- Distribute the student response pages and ask students to draw some of their initial designs in the top section.

- Instruct students to plan and construct their courses, then test them out.

- Circulate among the groups to provide guidance, answer questions, and facilitate discussions about the designs.

Testing (15 min)

Encourage the groups to create at least three different designs and test them. Is their game able to be won? Is it too easy or too hard? Guide them with questions and encourage them to try lots of different things.

Students record the details of their games on their response sheets. They should then combine features of their different designs to create their final, best design configuration to share with the rest of the class.

Circulate among the groups to help facilitate their discussions and decision process.

Have students draw and note the changes made for their final designs on the student response sheets.

D.I.Y. Arcade

Class Discussion (15 min)

- Bring the class back together to share and discuss.
- Discuss the design process with the class. Engineers try different solutions to engineering problems and test those solutions in order to come up with improved designs.
- Have groups share their best designs and talk about what worked for them and what didn't work.
- Allow other groups to comment or ask questions.
- Ask guiding questions to help student reflect on their designs:
    - What did you try first?
    - What changes did you make?
    - What was the most challenging aspect of constructing your game? Why?
    - Did you encounter any problems or unexpected issues during the construction process? How did you handle those problems?
    - What did you learn from the process?
    - How did working in a group impact the design and evaluation process? What were the advantages and challenges of collaborating on this project?

D.I.Y. Arcade

Optional: Group Work: Phase 2

If you have enough time, you can allow small groups to use their new knowledge to improve their arcade games.

If you have limited time, you can ask the students what improvements or modifications they would make if they were to build their games again based on what they learned from the other groups in the class.

Conclusion (5 minutes)

Recap the key concepts learned during the activity, emphasizing the engineering design process steps of discussion, design, testing, and redesign.

Encourage students to think about how they were able to improve their designs through trying different things.

Point out books in the classroom or school library that relate to games, engineering, physics, and other related topics.

Review the vocabulary words: "gravity" and "force."

Collect the student response sheets.

D.I.Y. Arcade

 Build an arcade game!

HERE ARE SOME IDEAS!

- Skeeball
- Claw machine
- Whack-a-mole
- Pinball
- Basketball game

- Air hockey
- Plinko
- Coin pusher
- Pool
- (Velcro) darts

As a group, you will build an arcade game. Try different designs to see what works best!

1. Choose which type of game you'd like to build.

2. Select a large cardboard box to build the game on.

3. Discuss how gravity will affect your game. Is there a ball that needs to move against gravity? How will this work?

4. Gather materials and set up your arcade game.

5. Try your game! Move things and try different materials until it works well.

6. Draw your first three attempts and note what changes you made.

7. Use what you have learned to create one more, final design. Draw it on your response sheet and be prepared to share it with the class.

Names: _____

D . I . Y . A r c a d e

Follow the directions to take on the challenge!

Design 1	Design 2	Design 3
	What we changed: _____ _____	What we changed: _____ _____

Final Design

What we changed:
_____
_____
_____

What configuration worked best? Why?

_____
_____
_____
_____
_____
_____
_____

D.I.Y. Arcade

Extension Activities

- Discuss the games that your students have seen at arcades. What are their favorites? What makes them fun?

- Invite another class to come and try your arcade! If you class is "buddies" with another class, this is a great activity for kids to do together. You can have your students make tickets and a slot in each game to feed tickets through. Students can make some prizes or a special award for kids who have earned tickets by playing their game in the d.i.y. arcade!

- Make a photobooth to go with the arcade.

- Take a field trip to an arcade to see the real thing in action.

- Do more demonstrations of gravity, such as dropping objects of different weights at the same height or using the force of magnetism to work against gravity.

- Invite a guest speaker that is an inventor, product engineer, mechanical engineer, or physicist to discuss gravity, forces, or the design process.

- Before or after this lesson, kids may enjoy seeing the video and learning more about Caine's arcade: thekidshouldseethis.com/post/caines-arcade-video. This video inspired a non-profit organization.

- Check out some more game examples at Kid Museum: kid-museum.org/make-it/kid-arcade/

D.I.Y. Arcade

Resources

- For teacher inspiration, check out this TED Talk: ted.com/talks/sir_ken_robinson_do_schools_kill_creativity
- Students may enjoy watching the TED-Ed video: ed.ted.com/lessons/jon-bergmann-how-to-think-about-gravity
- Read or provide some of the following books for your class:
  - Cardboard Box Engineering: Cool, Inventive Projects for Tinkerers, Makers & Future Scientists by Jonathan Adolph
  - Hardy Boys Trouble at the Arcade by Franklin W. Dixon
  - Gravity is a Mystery by Dr. Franklin M. Branley
  - The Gravity Tree by Anna Crowley Redding
  - Gravity: Mass, Energy, and the Force that Holds Things Together with Hands-on Science by Cindy Blobaum
  - The Creativity Project by Colby Sharp
  - Upcycle It! Crafts for Kids by Jennifer Perkins
  - Mechanical Engineering for Makers by Brian Bunnell
  - Tinkering: Kids Learn by Making Stuff by Curt Gabrielson
  - National Geographic Kids: Make This! Building Thinking, and Tinkering Projects for the Amazing Maker in You by Ella Schwartz

Snack
Grabber

Snack Grabber

Lesson

Snack Grabber: Engaging Engineering Design

Objectives

Students will:

- Invent a snack grabber using common materials.
- Compare and evaluate multiple design solutions according to the goal of reaching and retrieving a snack high on the wall.
- Apply the engineering design principles to test, discuss, evaluate, and redesign their structures.

Materials

- Wrapping paper tubes, broom sticks, other similar items
- Painter's tape
- Cups, rubber bands, straws
- Snacks (one per kid)
- Measuring tape
- Cardboard scraps
- Other materials
- Printed student instructions and response sheets (per group)

Vocabulary

- Invent
- Reach
- Engineering design
- Iteration

Snack Grabber

Introduction

It is fun to set this challenge up ahead of time! Set up enough snacks for your kids when they are not in the room (before class or during recess). You can use a circle of painter's tape to stick each treat to the wall as high as you can reach. Some good treats for this lesson include fruit roll-ups or small lollipops.

As students enter the room, they will notice the treats way up high! Let them know that they will be working in small groups to **invent** a device that can retrieve the snacks. The main rule is: their feet can not leave the ground! (So, no climbing on anything or jumping to reach the treat). Show them the materials they can use for their inventions.

The Challenge

Let the students know that the engineering challenge today is to work together and invent a snack grabber. They will use the materials available to get the snack from high on the wall. They should try to get the treat down safely without knocking it down.

They will try three different designs until they arrive at one final design that works best. Trying designs, making changes, and improving their product is called **iteration** and it is part of the engineering design process.

Because there are enough snacks for each student, they should be able to try several designs in their groups. Remind students that they will each get a treat no matter if their design is successful or not. (You may want to have a few extra in case some treats are broken in the process of this lesson).

Encourage the students to experiment with different designs.

Snack Grabber

Group Work: Phase 1 (15 min)

- Divide students into small groups of 3-4 people.

- Distribute materials to each group.

- Distribute the student response pages and ask students to draw some of their initial designs in the top section.

- Instruct students to plan and construct their snack grabbers.

- Circulate among the groups to provide guidance, answer questions, and facilitate discussions about the designs.

Testing (10 min)

Encourage the groups to create at least three different designs and assess each one's **reach**. Is it long enough to be able to get the treat down? Can it get it down safely, without breaking it?

Students draw their designs on their response sheets and record the changes they made for each iteration.

Have the groups combine features of their different designs to create their final, best design configuration to share with the rest of the class.

Circulate among the groups to help facilitate their discussions and decision process.

Have students draw and note the details about their final design on the student response sheets.

Snack Grabber

Class Discussion (15 min)

- Bring the class back together to share and discuss.
- Discuss the design process with the class. Engineers try different solutions to engineering problems and test those solutions in order to come up with improved designs.
- Have groups share their best designs and talk about what worked for them and what didn't work.
- Allow other groups to comment or ask questions.
- Ask guiding questions to help student reflect on their designs:
  - How did you decide on the design of your snack grabber?
  - What factors did you consider?
  - What was the most challenging aspect of building your grabber? Why?
  - Did you encounter any problems or unexpected issues during the invention process? How did you handle those problems?
  - What changes did you make to improve your initial designs?
  - How did working in a group impact the design and evaluation process? What were the advantages and challenges of collaborating on this project?

Snack Grabber

Optional: Group Work: Phase 2

If you have enough time, you can allow small groups to use their new knowledge to design one more snack grabber.

If you have limited time, you can ask the students what improvements or modifications they would make if they were to build the grabber again based on what they learned from the other groups in the class.

Conclusion (5 minutes)

Recap the key concepts learned during the activity, emphasizing the importance of trying different solutions to a problem.

Go over the engineering design process steps of discussion, design, testing, and redesign.

Encourage students to think about how engineering principles impact the best design.

Point out books in the classroom or school library that relate to engineering, invention, and other related topics.

Review the vocabulary words: invention, reach, and iteration.

Collect the student response sheets.

Snack Grabber

Follow the directions to take on the challenge!

As a group, you will invent your own snack grabber!

1. Discuss how to get the candy down. Remember your feet can not leave the ground! How can you get the candy without letting it fall?

2. Think about the reach your snack grabber needs to have. How long does it need to be?

3. Think about how to catch the candy. What materials could you use?

4. Try three different designs.

5. Draw your designs and write down what change you made for each iteration on the response sheet.

6. Discuss what you have learned from your three initial designs.

7. Decide upon your final design using what you have learned.

8. Build your final design.

9. Draw and note the changes of your final design on the student response sheet.

10. Write about what configuration worked best and why.

11. Prepare to share your design with the class!

Student Response Sheet

Names: _____

Snack Grabber

Follow the directions to take on the challenge!

Design 1

Design 2

What we changed:

_____
_____

Design 3

What we changed:

_____
_____

Final Design

What we changed:

_____
_____
_____

What configuration worked best? Why?

_____
_____
_____
_____
_____
_____
_____

Snack Grabber

Extension Activities

- Brainstorm what other purposes the snack grabber could serve. Could it turn on a light from five feet away? Could it scratch your back? What other uses could it have?

- Consider if the opposite problem needed to be solved. What if the candy had to be lifted up from the floor to the top of the wall. Could your snack grabber do this? If not, what modifications would make this possible?

- Take a field trip to an engineering firm to learn more about the engineering design process.

- Take a field trip to a local department store that has household items. Discuss what household tools you find and consider how they were invented.

- Invite a guest speaker that is an inventor, product engineer, mechanical engineer, or biomedical engineer to discuss inventions.

- Browse the Guinness Book of World Records records related to food and drink for some amazing wonders! www.guinnessworldrecords.com/records/showcase/food-and-drink

Snack Grabber

- For teacher inspiration, check out this TED Talk: www.ted.com/talks/saul_griffith_everyday_inventions

- Students may enjoy watching the TED-Ed Video: ed.ted.com/lessons/how-inventions-change-history-for-better-and-for-worse-kenneth-c-davis

- Read or provide some of the following books for your class to explore:

    - Inventions: A Visual Encyclopedia by DK Smithsonian

    - Timelines of Everything by DK Smithsonian

    - 1,000 Inventions and Discoveries by DK Smithsonian

    - 125 Cool Inventions: Supersmart Machines and Wacky Gadgets You Never Knew You Wanted! By National Geographic Kids

    - Girls Think of Everything: Stories of Ingenious Inventions by Women by Catherine Timmesh

    - Candy Bomber: The Story of the Berlin Airlift's "Chocolate Pilot" by Michael O. Tunnell

    - The Legend of the Candy Cane by Lori Walburg

    - Brain Candy: 500 Sweet Facts to Satisfy Your Curiosity by Julie Beer

    - The Candy Smash by Jacqueline Davies

    - The Candymakers by Wendy Mass

Innate
Press

Download the Freebies!

Scan to go to the website:

Then scroll to the bottom of the page.

Or visit:

innatepress.com/teaching-kids-the-
engineering-design-process

Credits

Borders:

Deeder Do Designs

You May Also Like

If your students enjoy these lessons, they may also enjoy some of our other books that are focused on topics such as science, symmetry, telling time, secret codes, and more!

Visit our author page to see more titles:
amazon.com/author/innatepress

Innate
Press

Keep in touch!

Visit our website:
innatepress.com

Or join our email list:
www.innatepress.com/
join-our-newsletter

To be the first to know
about our new books!

Find fun freebies here:

innatepress.com/secretfreebies

Made in the USA
Coppell, TX
27 October 2024

39220108R00072